Ellianna and Flynn: You are our whole world.
Your dad and I will always be there to cheer you on.
We love you always and are so proud of you both.
Love, Lindsay (Mom)

To my sweet, little Victor: I can't wait to see what
colorful adventures we will have together.
Love, Andra (Mom)

WRITTEN BY LINDSAY ACHTMAN

My Proudest Moment

ILLUSTRATED BY ANDRA PANA

My eyes are wide with wonder.

I see my heroes for the first time.
Their moves are like magic, filled
with power and grace.

I begin prancing around my yard,
chanting numbers to my stuffed animals.

I bumble through each spin and jump,
but I never give up!

4

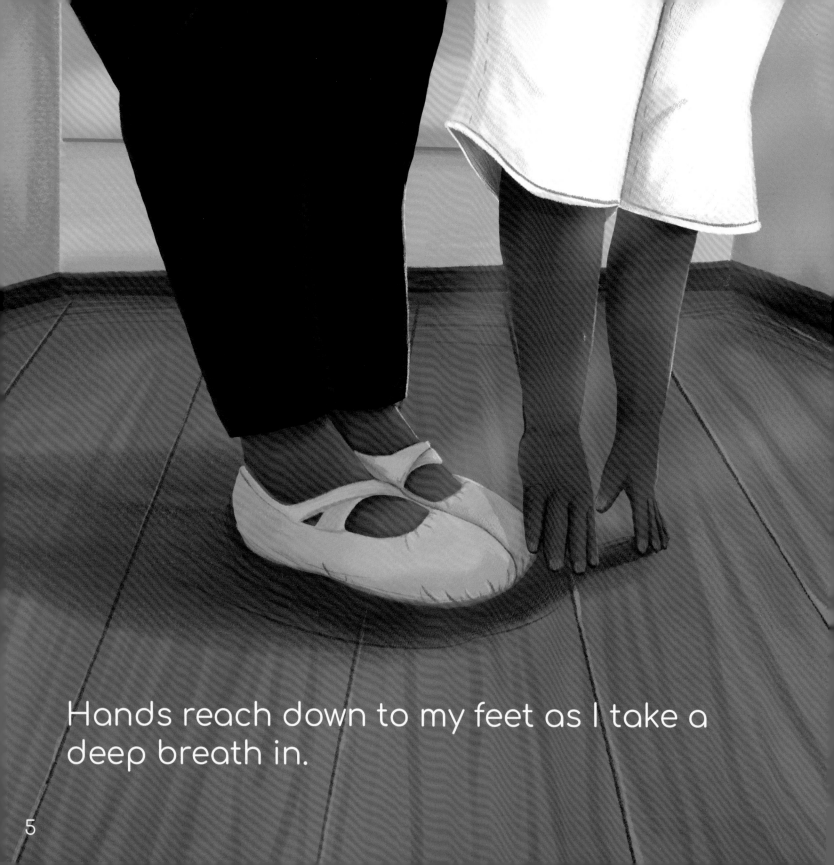

Hands reach down to my feet as I take a deep breath in.

My coach helps me focus as I begin to feel the rhythm in my body.

Practices become performances.
Nerves turn to joy.

Stumbling and giggling through each move I can feel myself improving.

Rehearsing day and night has prepared me for this moment.

My muscles power through, making me stronger than ever before.

The announcer begins to speak,
and my feet move into position.

BOOM   BOOM   BOOM

My heart pounds like a drum in my ears!

Anticipation builds, and so do my jitters.

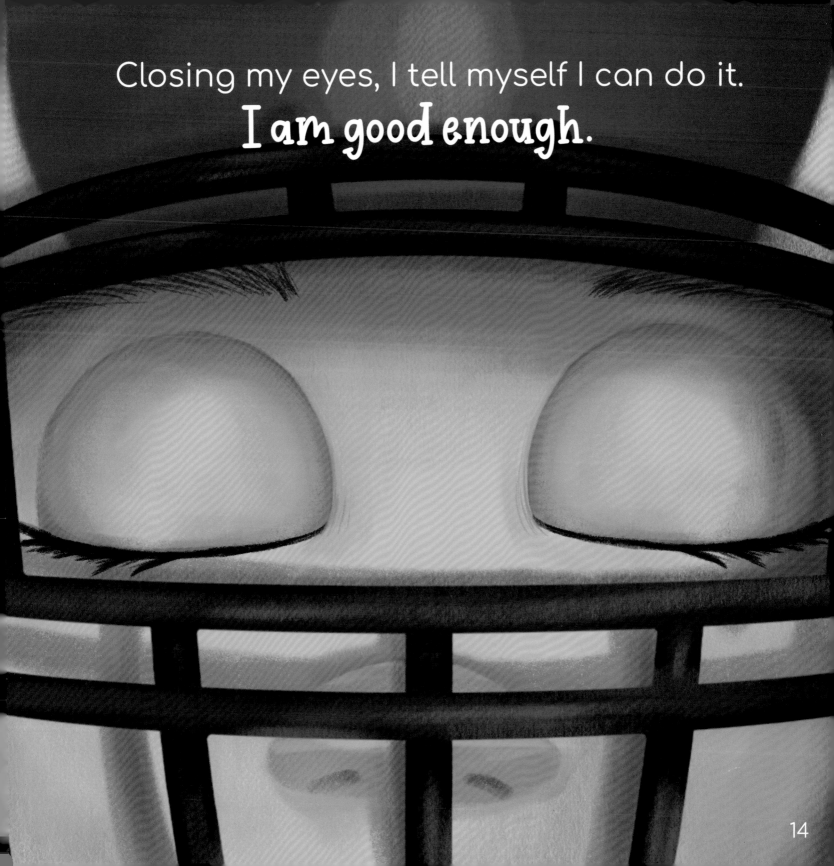

Closing my eyes, I tell myself I can do it.
I am good enough.

Exchanging fierce looks, we prepare to move as one.

Locking eyes with my teammate,
I'm shining with newfound confidence.
Exhaling slowly, I spring into action!

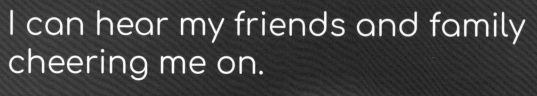

I can hear my friends and family cheering me on.

The louder the cheers,
the more energized I become!

My legs feel light as I soar through the air.

I float through space as time stops
for a moment.

I prepare for the biggest kick of the night.

My foot swings up with a giant WHOOSH!

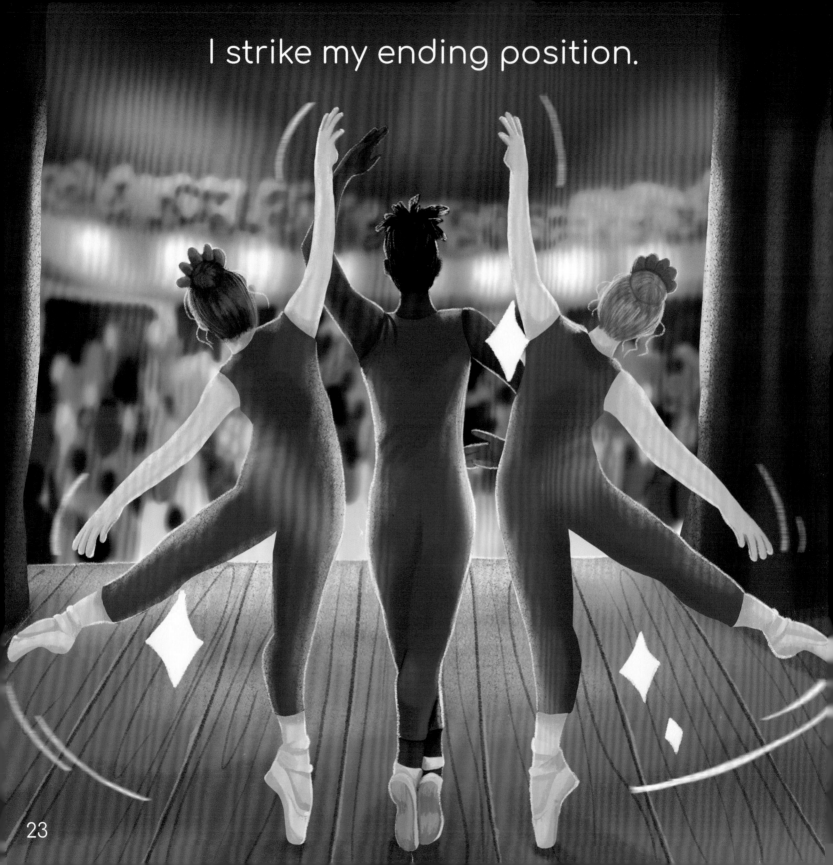

I strike my ending position.

My eyes tear up as the crowd goes wild!

24

I pause to take in the feelings
of exhaustion and joy.

My coach gives me a big high five!

My hard work has led me to this
incredible moment.

29

Win or lose...
I'M SO PROUD TO BE ME!

30

Inspiring Stories

Rebecca Longo
First female to receive a football scholarship

Prior to being known as the first female to receive a football scholarship, I was just an Arizona high school athlete who attempted any and every sport I could. For 5 years, I was the only female on all of my football teams. Those years were anything but ordinary; I faced many obstacles being a girl in what was considered a man's sport. Others disapproved but if it wasn't for the love and support from my close family and friends I would not have accomplished all that I did. When I was 18 years old I was recognized as the first female to receive a football scholarship. A short 2 years later I had the honor of doing what every kid dreams about, scoring the winning points during a championship game.

My biggest take away from my experiences is knowing that you won't always be the most gifted in the room but you can always be the hardest worker.

If you are determined and never quit, the places you'll go will be unimaginable!

**Readers, can you find Rebecca Longo hiding in our story?
Look for the "Number 4"

Danté Henderson
Professional Entertainer, Choreographer at Royal Caribbean

I grew up with an amazing home life, for the most part. We were not rich by any means, but we were close, and we were happy. Since I can remember, music has always been a huge part of my life. It has been the drive of my existence. From childhood, whenever I heard music, I would instinctively start to move and sing. It became my first love, and it wasn't long before I started to dream of performing for others and sharing my love of music. I used to choreograph little dance routines for Halloween, and I would use other kids from the neighborhood, including my younger sister, as dancers. None of us were trained, not one of us had ever taken a dance class. But we all worked hard and for me it paid off. I was 15 years old when I was invited to attend Hollywood High School of Performing Arts. It changed my whole life. Up until that point in my school life, I was always a loner. I was bullied and picked on. Other kids called me names, beat me up and harassed me constantly. Unbeknownst to my loving family, it was a nightmare that I lived with for many years. But Hollywood High would open my eyes to a world I had only dreamed of my entire life. It was there that I learned how deeply I loved to dance, and I jumped in, all in. Slowly I began feeling confident. I would practice my dancing in the alley behind our home. I didn't care about the guys at the other end playing basketball being able to see me, even though they would heckle me from time to time. Over the years I have heard it all when it comes to derogatory comments towards males who dance, particularly ballet dancers. But, in truth, we are a special breed of male altogether. I have gone on to dance and perform with some of the biggest names in the entertainment industry and I'm still going strong today.

Never give up your power, never give up your dream!

Conor Holloway
Dancer + Social Media & Content Strategist American Ballet Theatre

Photograph by: James Jin

My first experience with ballet was at the age of thirteen. I went to an audition for The Nutcracker at the Louisville Ballet in Kentucky. It was the first time and place I had ever seen professional dancers up close. It took all of eight seconds for me to be completely absorbed by ballet and my hopeful future as a professional dancer. Although the artistry and the athleticism of the male dancers was impressive, it was really the powerful sensitivity and articulation of the ballerinas that hooked me. During the majority of my training years, I doubted my ability to be "masculine enough" for ballet and for the princely roles I was told to aspire towards. Even as a student, I felt like I was playing a character. But for the love of ballet, I persisted. It wasn't until my third or fourth year as a professional dancer with American Ballet Theatre living in New York City that I considered the idea of relinquishing the male gender construct that had robbed me of so much joy in the studio and on stage. After I came out as non-binary, I came to the conclusion that dance and music are transcendent of gender and exist in a plane above words and constructs. So I finally gave myself the permission to embrace every facet of myself; no matter how sensitive, athletic, or artistic. Working as the only gender non-conforming dancer in a major institution can feel isolating and I still have moments of fear and anxiety for what others may perceive. A few weeks ago, I had my mid-year evaluation after nine years of dancing with ABT and my director shared with me that ever since I came out, he witnessed a remarkable freedom and versatility in my dancing that he had never seen before.

Giving yourself the permission to take space and embrace yourself is not only expansive for yourself but can inspire growth in others as well.
Shine on, my friends.

My Proudest Moment!

Your story is just beginning!
Write your own "Proudest Moment" story.
Get ready to inspire the world

Lindsay Achtman is a passionate teacher and loving mother of two.
She uses playful language as she invites you to enter a world full of possibilities.
Lindsay hopes that her stories will bring people together and help create a
more accepting world. This is Lindsay and Andra's second book together as they
have teamed up in the past to create the magnificent story, "I Hope It's A Puppy!"

Andra is a child wandering through the magic land of colors, with an MA and BA
in her pocket and a paintbrush in her hand. Inspired by the amazing little girls
at her art course, and her son, she discovered that she loves drawing for kids.
Andra loves to be surrounded by magical characters as she gets to know the
story of every hero and meets storytellers from all around the world.